DREAMWORKS
TROLLHUNTERS
TALES OF ARCADIA
FROM GUILLERMO DEL TORO

DREAMWORKS
TROLLHUNTERS
TALES OF ARCADIA
FROM GUILLERMO DEL TORO

THE SECRET HISTORY OF TROLLKIND

Script by
**MARC GUGGENHEIM &
RICHARD HAMILTON**

Art by
TIMOTHY GREEN II

Coloring by
WES DZIOBA

Lettering by
RICHARD STARKINGS
and Comicraft's
JIMMY BETANCOURT

Cover Art by
BILL SIENKIEWICZ

Dark Horse Books

editor
FREDDYE MILLER

collection designer
JUSTIN COUCH

assistant editor
KEVIN BURKHALTER

digital art technician
ALLYSON HALLER

Neil Hankerson, Executive Vice President · Tom Weddle, Chief Financial Officer · Randy Stradley, Vice President of Publishing · Nick McWhorter, Chief Business Development Officer · Matt Parkinson, Vice President of Marketing · Dale LaFountain, Vice President of Information Technology · Cara Niece, Vice President of Production and Scheduling · Mark Bernardi, Vice President of Book Trade and Digital Sales · Ken Lizzi, General Counsel · Dave Marshall, Editor in Chief · Davey Estrada, Editorial Director · Chris Warner, Senior Books Editor · Cary Grazzini, Director of Specialty Projects · Lia Ribacchi, Art Director · Vanessa Todd, Director of Print Purchasing · Matt Dryer, Director of Digital Art and Prepress · Michael Gombos, Director of International Publishing and Licensing · Kari Yadro, Director of Custom Programs

Special thanks to Rodrigo Blaas, A.C. Bradley, Corinne Combs, Marc Guggenheim, Dan Hageman, Kevin Hageman, Lawrence "Shifty" Hamashima, Chad Hammes, Kelly Kulchak, Barbara Layman, Christina Steinberg, Mike Sund, John Tanzer, Andrew Tolbert, Alex Ward, and Susan Weber at DreamWorks Animation and Universal Studios.

Published by Dark Horse Books
A division of Dark Horse Comics, Inc.
10956 SE Main Street
Milwaukie, OR 97222

DarkHorse.com

International Licensing: 503-905-2377
To find a comics shop in your area, visit comicshoplocator.com

Names: Guggenheim, Marc, author. | Hamilton, Richard, author. | Green, Timothy, II, 1975- artist. | Dzioba, Wes, colourist. | Comicraft, letterer. | Sienkiewicz, Bill, artist.
Title: Trollhunters : the secret history of trollkind / script by Marc Guggenheim & Richard Hamilton ; art by Timothy Green II ; coloring by Wes Dzioba ; lettering by Comicraft ; cover art by Bill Sienkiewicz.
Description: First edition. | Milwaukie, OR : Dark Horse Books, 2018. | Summary: "When fifteen-year-old teenager Jim Lake, Jr. stumbled upon a magical amulet, it gave him a powerful suit of armor and the title of Trollhunter--defender of the good Trolls. In one training session, Jim's Troll companion, Blinky, must detail the battles of Kanjigar the Courageous--his struggles, triumphs, and failures in leading the safety of Troll Market!"-- Provided by publisher.
Identifiers: LCCN 2017045876 | ISBN 9781506702896 (paperback)
Subjects: LCSH: Graphic novels. | CYAC: Graphic novels. | Trolls--Fiction. | Magic--Fiction. | BISAC: JUVENILE FICTION / Comics & Graphic Novels / Media Tie-In. | JUVENILE FICTION / Comics & Graphic Novels / General.
Classification: LCC PZ7.7.G84 Tr 2018 | DDC 741.5/973--dc23
LC record available at https://lccn.loc.gov/2017045876

HUMAN TEENAGER JIM LAKE, JR.
POSSESSES THE MAGICAL AMULET THAT
GRANTS HIM ACCESS TO A POWERFUL SUIT OF
ARMOR AND THE MONUMENTAL RESPONSIBILITY
OF TROLLHUNTER—DEFENDER OF THE GOOD
TROLLS. ALONG WITH HIS FRIENDS—BOTH
HUMAN AND TROLL—HE TRAINS TO FIGHT
FOR THE TROLLS THAT LIVE BENEATH HIS
HOMETOWN OF ARCADIA OAKS.

TROLLMARKET. THE HERO'S FORGE.

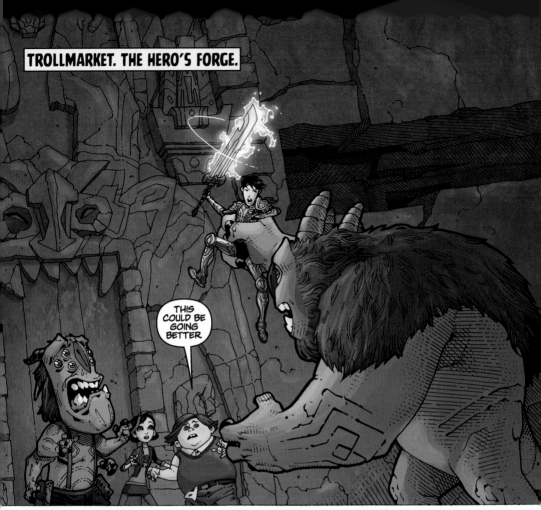

THIS COULD BE GOING BETTER

INDEED. THOUGH IF THERE WERE NO ROOM FOR IMPROVEMENT, THERE WOULD BE NO NEED FOR TRAINING.

EXCELLENT, MASTER JIM! YOU HAVE HIM RIGHT WHERE YOU WANT HIM!

7

I SAID "ALONG OUR *PRESENT* COURSE."

WHAT'S NEEDED HERE IS AN INSPIRATIONAL RECITATION OF--

--TROLL *LORE.*

DON'T SAY "TROLL HISTORY."

PLEASE NOT ANOTHER HISTORY LESSON...

AT LEAST IT BEATS GETTING BEATEN UP.

THAT'S SADLY TRUE.

HISTORY IS NEVER SAD, MASTER JIM.

YOU CAN DRAW BOTH SOLACE AND INSPIRATION FROM THE FACT THAT YOU ARE ONLY THE LATEST IN A LONG LINE OF TROLLHUNTERS.

EACH OF WHOM FACED CHALLENGES AS GREAT OR EVEN GREATER THAN THE ONE YOU FACE NOW.

INDEED, EVEN DRAAL'S OWN FATHER--

KANJIGAR THE COURAGEOUS.

--SUFFERED MANY CRISES OF SELF-CONFIDENCE.

SEE, JIMBO? EVEN KANJIGAR

WHAT TYPES OF CRISES?

WOULD YOU BELIEVE THAT EVEN THE GREAT KANJIGAR DOUBTED HIS FITNESS TO HOLD THE MANTLE OF TROLLHUNTER?

IN FACT, I *WOULD* BELIEVE IT.

"THE END OF THE THREAT OF THE GUMM-GUMMS.

"I SPEAK, OF COURSE, OF THE GREAT BATTLE OF *KILLAHEAD BRIDGE.*"

"I WAS THERE THAT FATEFUL NIGHT AND FOUGHT QUITE GALLANTLY.

PLEASE DON'T EAT ME!!!

"DRAAL FOUGHT SIDE-BY-SIDE WITH HIS FATHER KANJIGAR, WHO HAD YET TO BE CHOSEN AS THE TROLLHUNTER AMULET'S MASTER

"THAT MANTLE WAS CARRIED MOST ABLY BY..."

OOO! OOO! I KNOW THAT ONE!

IT'S DEYA THE DELIVERER!

INDEED, TOBY D.

DON'T INTERRUPT ME AGAIN.

BUT DEYA HAD NOT EARNED THE NAME "DELIVERER" BY THIS POINT.

"NOR HAD AAARRRGGHH!!! RENOUNCED THE GUMM-GUMM PATH.

"UNTIL THAT FATEFUL NIGHT."

"WHEN UPON SEEING KANJIGAR AT BULAR'S MERCY...

"...HE HEARD THE CALL OF HIS CONSCIENCE."

FATHER!!!

"IN A CERTAIN FORM.

"AND, IN THAT MOMENT, AAARRRGGHH!!! CHANGED SIDES."

"HE *CLASHED* WITH THE MIGHTY BULAR...

"...AND DEALT HIM AN EVEN *MIGHTIER* BLOW."

KACHOK

AND RAN.

INDEED.

"SO GREAT WAS AAARRGGHH!!!'S INNER TURMOIL, HE FLED FROM THE FIELD OF BATTLE, TORN AND CONFLICTED."

"BULAR GAVE CHASE.

"AND THAT IS WHY NEITHER WAS PRESENT FOR...THE CONVERGENCE."

WHAT'S THE CONVERGENCE?

WHAT DID I SAY ABOUT INTERRUPTING?

NOT TO.

PRECISELY.

"THE CONVERGENCE IS WHAT HAS BECOME KNOWN AS THE MOMENT WHEN DEYA MANAGED TO STRIKE A CRITICAL BLOW AGAINST GUNMAR.

"AND THEN PLACED HER AMULET WITHIN THE STONE OF KILLAHEAD BRIDGE..."

19

"ALAS, IT WAS A BITTERSWEET VICTORY, AS IT APPEARED MY BROTHER--"

"WAIT. YOU'VE GOT A *BROTHER?*"

RIGHT. NO INTERRUPTING. GOT IT.

"MY BROTHER, DICTATIOUS GALADRIGAL.

"APPARENTLY, HE FELL IN THE COURSE OF BATTLE."

AND I WOULD NEVER SEE HIM AGAIN.

SO PROFOUND WAS MY GRIEF I BARELY HEARD DEYA ORDER US TO DISMANTLE THE KILLAHEAD BRIDGE SO GUNMAR AND HIS HORDE COULD *NEVER* ESCAPE FROM THEIR EXILE IN THE DARKLANDS.

DISMANTLE THE KILLAHEAD BRIDGE SO GUNMAR AND HIS HORDE CAN *NEVER* ESCAPE FROM THEIR EXILE IN THE DARKLANDS.

"THE PIECES WERE TAKEN BY SEVERAL VOLUNTEER TROLLS AND SCATTERED TO THE FOUR CORNERS OF THE EARTH.

"CENTURIES PASSED--"

"WAITAMINUTE..."

CENTURIES? THE KILLAHEAD BRIDGE IS DISMANTLED AND THE GUMM-GUMMS ARE BANISHED.

ISN'T THE STORY OVER?

IT'S THE STORYTELLER WHO DETERMINES THE TALE'S CONCLUSION, MASTER JIM.

WE HAVEN'T EVEN GOTTEN TO THE PART WHERE KANJIGAR ASSUMES THE MANTLE YOU FEEL UNWORTHY TO BEAR.

WELL, I NEVER SAID--

NO INTERRUPTING. SORRY.

NOW, AS I WAS SAYING...

"CENTURIES PASSED.

"AND A FEEBLE TRUCE--KNOWN AS 'THE PACT'--WAS STRUCK BETWEEN MANKIND AND TROLLKIND.

"*BUT* AS THE YEARS WENT BY, A CONSERVATIVE SEGMENT OF TROLLS GREW RESTLESS.

"THEY LONGED FOR THE GUMM-GUMMS' BRUTALITY AND STRENGTH. THEY BELIEVED THE PACT MADE US LOOK WEAK. THAT HUMANS 'LOOKED DOWN' UPON US.

"AND AS THIS HAPPENED, THE HEARTSTONE--THE SOURCE OF OUR HOME'S SUSTENANCE AND VITALITY--BEGAN TO WANE."

"WE TROLLS COMMITTED TO LIMIT OUR DIET TO CATS AND USED ARTICLES OF CLOTHING..."

"GOOD FIBER"

"INDEED.

"WANE?"

"MEANS 'DIMINISH AND GROW WEAKER.'

"IT WAS TIME TO VENTURE FORTH TO A NEW HOME, A NEW LAND. A LAND OF HOPE AND POSSIBILITIES UNLIMITED.

"FOR VENDEL SENSED A NEW--PERHAPS ALL-POWERFUL--HEARTSTONE...IN A PLACE HUMANS CALLED..."

"...THE NEW WORLD."

THIS FLOATING HUMAN MARKET SETS SAIL AT SUNRISE.

WHICH DOESN'T GIVE US MUCH TIME. TREAD LIGHTLY. AND MAKE *HASTE*.

WORRY NOT, DEYA.

ALTHOUGH SURFACE VILLAGES LIKE THIS "PLYMOUTH" SEEM UNSETTLING, EVEN LAUGHABLE, TO US--WE TROLLS REMAIN SUPREMELY COMFORTABLE UNDER COVER OF DARKNESS.

THAT'S WHAT WORRIES ME.

FOR I SENSE *DANGER*.

TROLLHUNTER!

CRE-ACK

THE SCION OF GUNMAR WOULD WASH AWAY OLD GRIEVANCES--

--WITH A RIVER OF YOUR **BLOOD!**

ALL OF YOU--TO THE MAYFLOWER.

I'LL DEAL WITH BULAR.

CLANG

DEYA! DRAAL THE DEADLY STANDS FAST AT YOUR SIDE--

NO! OUR TROLLHUNTER'S GIVEN US A CHANCE AT SURVIVAL. LET'S NOT SQUANDER IT.

BUT, FATHER, SHE-- SHE'S ONE OF US...

"YES, SON. AND WHAT SHE DOES-- SHE DOES FOR *ALL* OF US."

YOU FOUGHT HARDER AT KILLAHEAD, TROLLHUNTER

NOT ENOUGH *FLESHLING* IN YOUR DIET NOW?

THE THOUGHT OF VANQUISHING YOU IS ALL THE NOURISHMENT I NEED, GUMM-GUMM.

STEP THE MAST SMARTLY, LADS!

SHEET HOME AND RAISE ANCHOR!

MAKE READY TO SET SAIL!

THE HUMANS ARE PUNCTUAL, I'LL GIVE THEM THAT.

THAT'S IT, TROLLHUNTER-- *RUN!*

I'LL HOUND YOU DOWN AS I HAVE ACROSS THIS LAND! ACROSS CENTURIES!

GOOD...

...I HAD HOPED AS MUCH.

THOOM

IT WOULD SEEM NEITHER OF US SHALL SET FOOT ON THE NEW WORLD, BULAR.

A SMALL PRICE TO PAY--

"--FOR THE SAFE PASSAGE OF MY PEOPLE."

BLINKOUS, DO YOU SEE DEYA?

SHE'S DRIFTED FROM VIEW, VENDEL.

I PRAY TO GORGUS WE'VE DONE THE RIGHT THING...

MAY MERLIN GRANT YOU GREATER MERCY THAN ANY *YOU* HAVE SHOWN, BULAR.

MERCY?

NO. NO MERCY...

BUT I OFFER *BLINDING SUNLIGHT* INSTEAD...

AAAGH!

A PITY YOU CAN'T *WATCH* ME SLAUGHTER YOUR KIND, TROLLHUNTER

I'M LOSING THEM, DRAAL. IF OUR PEOPLE WERE EVER MINE TO BEGIN WITH.

DEYA'S *DEAD*, FATHER. CLINGING TO HER GHOST DOES US NO FAVORS.

LEAST OF ALL *YOU.*

PERHAPS I MAY BE OF SOME SLIGHT ASSISTANCE, KANJIGAR! THE TROLLHUNTER MUST BE TRAINED AS MUCH IN LEADERSHIP AS IN COMBAT.

WASN'T UNKAR THE UNFORTUNATE THE LAST TO SUFFER YOUR "SLIGHT ASSISTANCE?"

I'LL HAVE YOU KNOW WE CALLED HIM UNKAR THE *ULTIMATE* DURING HIS TIME AS TROLLHUNTER!

ALL SIX HOURS OF IT...

DRAAL. BLINKY. *BEHOLD!*

LAND, HO!'

GREAT GRONKA MORKA!'

"BY DEYA'S GRACE, WE HAD FINALLY REACHED OUR DESTINATION--AND HELD UP OUR END OF THE PACT, DESPITE CONSIDERABLE TEMPTATION.

"PLYMOUTH ROCK, THE HUMANS CALLED THEIR NEW HOME. IT WAS NO HEARTSTONE, TO BE SURE.

"YET THE VERY SIGHT OF IT RAISED OUR SPIRITS AND GRANTED US THE VIGOR TO EMBARK UPON THE *NEXT* LEG OF OUR TREK..."

"...TO A PLACE CALLED 'NEW JERSEY.'

"WE KEPT MOVING.

"YEARS PASSED.

"OUR JOURNEY WAS TREACHEROUS."

"BUT WE SAW THE WIDE VARIETY OF HUMAN CULTURES THIS 'NEW WORLD' HAD TO OFFER.

"SOME WERE EVEN *USEFUL*.

"AS WERE SOME HUMANS.

"TWO GENTLEMEN NAMED 'LEWIS' AND 'CLARK' WERE PARTICULARLY HELPFUL IN GUIDING US ON OUR PATH."

DEVILS!

WHAT'RE THEY SAYING?

--LEAD US NOT INTO TEMPTATION, BUT DELIVER US FROM EVIL! FOR YOURS IS THE KINGDOM AND THE POWER AND--

I DUNNO. BUT TO THEM, WE MUST LOOK LIKE *ORLAGK THE OPPRESSOR* HIMSELF!

--THE GLORY?

"AMEN."

THINK ≈HUFF≈ WE LOST HIM!

WITH ALL THAT ARMOR ≈HUFF≈ NO WAY ≈HUFF≈ KANJIGAR CAN CATCH--

--UHHHFFF!

WHUP

WHUP

MASTERFULLY DONE, KANJIGAR! I WITNESSED YOUR ENTIRE *HUNT* FROM AFAR AND, WELL--SHEER PERFECTION.

THAT SAID, I *DO* HAVE A FEW NOTES...

I'LL TAKE THEM UNDER ADVISEMENT. LATER

OF COURSE. AND HAVE YOU CONSIDERED--

LATER.

NATURALLY. BUT IF I COULD JUST OFFER--

LATER.

"...BY A LITTLE.

"COULDN'T FIND ANOTHER SHIP.

"SAILORS ALL YELL *'AIEEE!'* WHEN SEE ME.

"SO WALKED.

"WALKED? *ALL* THIS TIME? ALL THIS *WAY?*"

"DEEP CAVE TROLLS PATIENT. AND GOOD WITH DIRECTIONS.

"MADE A *FEW* WRONG TURNS..."

...BUT FINALLY FOUND YOU.

A MISTAKE YOU'LL NOT LIKELY REPEAT, STRANGER.

I SAY WE *EXECUTE* HIM!

HE MAY HAVE FOUGHT AT KILLAHEAD, BUT CERTAINLY NOT ON *OUR* SIDE.

FOR ALL WE KNOW, HE MIGHT BE AN ADVANCE SCOUT FOR A *LARGER* FORCE OF ENEMY TROLLS!

WHY, I'D HAZARD THAT THE BUNDLE ON HIS BACK IS SOME SORT OF *WEAPON* TO BE USED AGAINST US!

NOT WEAPON.

GIFT.

HE'S THE ONE WHO SLAYED DEYA!

TRAITOR! TO *ALL* OF TROLLKIND!

TAKE HIM! IT'LL BE DEATH BY SUNLIGHT!

THEN I, TOO, SHALL PERISH AT DAYBREAK.

I CARE NOT WHAT YOU THINK. THIS TROLL ONCE RISKED HIS LIFE TO SAVE MY *OWN*.

I REPAY THAT KINDNESS NOW--AND EXPECT EACH OF YOU TO DO THE *SAME*.

VENDEL, YOU SIMPLY CANNOT ALLOW--

CONSIDER YOUR PROTESTATIONS DULY NOTED, BLINKOUS.

BUT OUR TROLLHUNTER'S WORD IS *LAW*. THE KRUBERA MAY STAY--

--ALBEIT AS AN *OUTCAST* ON THE VERY FRINGES OF OUR GROUP.

EASY, WISE ONE. I HAVE GOT YOU.

I'LL THANK YOU TO KINDLY KEEP YOUR TRAITOROUS HANDS TO YOURSELF!

"FROZEN FROM OUR HOOVES TO OUR HORNS AND DEPRIVED OF A HEARTSTONE'S RECUPERATIVE PROPERTIES, THE ORDEAL BROUGHT OUT THE WORST IN SOME OF US..."

THOUGHT I FELT AN ITCH.

TELL CRAGGEN-- WHAT MAKES YOU FOOLISH ENOUGH TO BELIEVE HE'D LET YOU SCALE HIS GLORIOUS FORM WITHOUT PAYMENT?

WE HAVE NO QUARREL WITH YOU, OLD ONE. MERELY DO AS YOUR TROLLHUNTER COMMANDS AND LET US PASS.

AH, NOW, NOW, KANJIGAR! NO NEED TO *ANTAGONIZE* A FELLOW TROLL!

ESPECIALLY ONE SO *LARGE*. LET ME HANDLE THIS DIPLOMATICALLY.

GREETINGS, CRAGGEN! I AM VENDEL, SON OF RUNDLE, SON OF KILFRED!

THOUGH THE MOUNTAIN TROLLS HAVE LONG SIDED WITH THE GUMM-GUMMS, I IMPLORE--

OH, I HAVE NO PROBLEM WITH YOU.

IT'S MY BROTHERS WHO HATE MERLIN-WORSHIPPERS.

KILFRED, EH? WE HEARD OF 'IM.

AND THAT HE WAS A REAL GLORK-HOLE.

AH. WELL. I TRIED...

A MOST *HEROIC* EFFORT, VENDEL. TRULY.

HURR, HURR, HURR! DO NOT POUT, INSIGNIFICANT THINGS--REJOICE!

THERE'S NO NEED TO PASS. YOU'VE REACHED YOUR NEW HOME AT LONG LAST!

HERE, YOU WILL GLADLY SERVE US FOR WHAT REMAINS OF YOUR FLEETING LIVES.

CONSIDER THAT YOUR PAYMENT FOR DARING TO CROSS CRAGGEN, GREATEST OF MOUNTAIN TROLLS, AND HIS BROTHERS THREE.

YOU MAY CAMP AT MY FEET AND REST FOR THE DAY. COME THE NEW MOON, MY BROTHERS AND I SHALL PUT YOU TO TASK.

AFTER COMING ALL THIS WAY, *THIS* IS OUR FATE?

TO *TOIL* INSIDE FOUR MOUNTAIN TROLLS UNTIL WE CRUMBLE TO DUST?

I COULD REALLY GO FOR A *CAT* RIGHT NOW!

ALAS, WHAT CHOICE HAVE WE? WE'VE BEEN APART FROM A HEARTSTONE FOR TOO LONG TO PUT UP MUCH OF A FIGHT. PERHAPS...

PERHAPS THIS WAS ALWAYS MEANT TO BE OUR *DESTINY.*

DESTINY?!

DESTINY IS A *GIFT.* DEYA GAVE ALL SHE HAD SO THAT WE MIGHT CONTINUE.

I WILL NOT SEE HER SACRIFICE GO TO WASTE.

KANJIGAR YOU ARE THE FINEST WARRIOR MY EYES HAVE EVER BEHELD--EVEN IF YOU NEVER *DID* LET ME TRAIN YOU. BUT TO THINK YOU *ALONE* CAN TAKE ON A FAMILY OF INBRED MOUNTAIN TROLLS?

IT'S *MADNESS!*

THE ONLY MADNESS WOULD BE FOR ME TO *GIVE UP* AND FAIL YOU, BLINKY--AND THE REST OF OUR KIND. I DON'T HAVE THAT KIND OF LUXURY, AS YOUR TROLLHUNTER

OR YOUR FRIEND.

AND HE *WON'T* BE ALONE.

THIS TIME, I STAND FAST AT MY TROLLHUNTER'S SIDE.

WHAT HE SAID.

SKRINK

KRAK

THE SUN HAS SET. WE THREE SHALL DO OUR BEST TO DISTRACT CRAGGEN AND HIS CLAN.

WHEN THE EARTH SHAKES, THAT'S YOUR SIGNAL TO ESCAPE.

FAREWELL, MY BROTHERS.

GO WITH GORGUS, TROLLHUNTER.

THOUGH I FEAR WE SHALL ALL SOON JOIN YOU IN THE VOID...

WHY?

THUMP

MAYBE FOR THE SAME REASON THOSE THREE TROLLS NOW MARCH INTO *CERTAIN DEATH!*

YOU MEAN THE *GUMM-GUMM*, DRAAL THE *DIM*, AND MERLIN'S *MISTAKE?*

THE ONE WHO WON'T EVEN LET US EAT HUMANS TO RENEW OUR STRENGTH?

I MEAN OUR *BROTHERS.* I UNDERSTAND YOU'RE *AFRAID*-- I AM, TOO!

BUT...BUT NEVER FORGET THAT FEAR IS BUT THE PRECURSOR TO VALOR

THAT TO *STRIVE* AND *TRIUMPH* IN THE FACE OF FEAR IS WHAT IT MEANS TO BE A *HERO.*

TO THINK, I'VE BEEN TRYING TO *TRAIN* OUR TROLLHUNTER--

--WHEN IT WAS HE WHO TAUGHT *ME* A LESSON. ONE I HOPE I HAVEN'T LEARNED TOO *LATE...*

RRRAAAHHH!

KWA-THOOM

ATTACK ONE MOUNTAIN TROLL AND YOU ATTACK US ALL! SO SWEARS BOULDERJAW!

URRK--

THE TIME FOR DISTRACTION IS OVER. THIS IS *WAR*.

THERE'S STILL FIGHT LEFT IN ME, FATHER

--BLLLAAAARRRGGG!

MERLIN PRESERVE US...

AARGHAUMONT, ARE YOU READY?

BLINKY! I'M THANKFUL YOU'VE JOINED US--BUT TO WHAT END?

IS IT THE OTHERS? ARE THEY IN *DANGER?*

OH, THEY LIVE, KANJIGAR.

THOUGH I SCARCELY KNOW HOW THEY'LL BE ABLE TO *LIVE WITH* THEMSELVES.

I OWE YOU A GREAT APOLOGY.

ALL OF YOU.

SOMETIMES, EVEN HAVING *SIX* EYES PREVENTS ONE FROM SEEING THE *TRUTH.*

I KNOW I'M NOT MUCH OF A WARRIOR! BUT IF I'M DYING TODAY--

WHA--?

--THEN THESE FOUR ARMS ARE GOING DOWN *SWINGING!*

NOW,
AAARRRGGHH!!!

--RAAAAHHHH!

RRRRR--

KA-KOOOOOM

SLOPEBROW!

BY GORGUS...
I THINK OUR ODDS
JUST WENT FROM
SUICIDAL TO
IMPOSSIBLE!

I
LIKE THOSE
ODDS.

AS DO **WE**.

YOU HONOR ME--AND DEYA'S MEMORY--WITH YOUR **COURAGE**, GOOD TROLLS.

NOW, **STEEL** YOURSELVES FOR BATTLE.

CHAK KA-CHAK

AND WHEN IN DOUBT...

WHISH WHISH

AAAIII-YYYEEEEE!

...ALWAYS KICK THEM IN THE **GRONK-NUKS**!

KRIK

KRIK

ACK

"IN TIME, OUR KIND CAME TO KNOW THIS BLOODY EVENT AS THE GREAT ROCKY MOUNTAIN TROLL WAR.

"OR G.R.M.T.W., FOR SHORT."

"ALTHOUGH WE LOST MANY TROLLS THAT DAY--SOME FRIENDS, SOME NOT, BUT ALL REMEMBERED--"

"--IT WAS THE BIRTH OF A *LEGEND*. BUT TO KANJIGAR..."

"...IT WAS *DUTY*."

I...ASK YOU... CRAGGEN...AS THE *LAST* OF YOUR *KIN*...DO YOU *YIELD*?

AYE, TROLLHUNTER... WE *YIELD*.

KAN-JI-GAR! KAN-JI-GAR! KAN-JI-GAR!

GLUG!

⇉HIC⇇

GLUG FOR ALL!

YOU NEEDN'T SIT AT THE FRINGES ANY LONGER, AARGHAUMONT.

ONCE AGAIN, YOU'VE PROVEN YOURSELF IN BATTLE.

THANKS. BUT BATTLE WAS *LAST* FOR ME.

NO MORE. AAARRRGGHH!!! NOW PACIFIC.

HAH! I BELIEVE YOU MEAN TO SAY *"PACIFIST,"* MY FRIEND.

SURE.

"MONTHS PASSED. AND WE ARRIVED IN A REALM KNOWN AS...'CALIFORNIA.'"

WELL? FATHER?

WE... WE HAVE ARRIVED.

SKRIK

CRACK ACK

FWASH

69

YES...WITH THE PROPER CARE AND CULTIVATION--A CUT HERE, A CLEAVE THERE...

...I BELIEVE THIS HEARTSTONE WILL GROW INTO THE FINEST OF THIS OR *ANY* LAND.

"VENDEL FELT IT IN HIS HORNS, JUST AS WE FELT THE YOUNG HEARTSTONE START TO RESTORE OUR ENERGY...

"...THIS WAS *HOME.*"

"DEYA MAY HAVE *DELIVERED* US TO THIS STRANGE CONTINENT...

"...BUT IT WAS KANJIGAR WHO *ENCOURAGED* US TO *SURVIVE* IT."

CAN THIS BE? EVEN IN VICTORY, DOES SOMETHING STILL *TROUBLE* OUR TROLLHUNTER?

NO, BLINKY, THOUGH I FEAR I MUST TROUBLE *YOU.*

I SEEK TO PAY TRIBUTE HERE TO DEYA--TO *ALL* OUR FALLEN TROLLHUNTERS--YET I REMAIN UNCERTAIN HOW.

ANY ADVICE?

WHY, KANJIGAR... THAT IS TO SAY, *MASTER* KANJIGAR...I BELIEVE I HAVE JUST THE IDEA!

"SO NOW YOU SEE, MASTER JIM. WHEN THE STATUES OF YOUR PREDECESSORS LOOK DOWN UPON YOU IN THE HERO'S FORGE, IT IS NOT WITH DISAPPOINTMENT.

"IT IS WITH *UNDERSTANDING.* EACH OF MERLIN'S CREATIONS HAVE FACED THEIR OWN UNIQUE CHALLENGES IN THEIR OWN UNIQUE WAYS.

"JUST AS *YOU* SHALL CONTINUE TO DO."

"FOR A TROLLHUNTER IS SO MUCH MORE THAN A WARRIOR"

FINALLY.

"TO BECOME A TROLLHUNTER IS TO BECOME PART OF A CONTINUANCE. A TRADITION."

THEY'RE HERE. I *SMELL* THE AMULET'S STENCH IN THE AIR.

AND HERE ALL I COULD SMELL WAS THE *MANURE.*

"A LEGACY THAT ENDURES IN THE SAME WAY ITS CHAMPIONS ENDURE."

THAT'S NOT ALL THAT STINKS HERE, *IMPURE.*

I RECKON I DON'T KNOW WHAT YOU MEAN, STRANGER

I'M BUT A HUMBLE *TEACHER* AT THE LOCAL SCHOOLHOUSE.

ALBEIT ONE WITH A MESSAGE FROM YOUR *FATHER...*

"FOR ALL TIME."

END.